To my
very special someone,

Debbi

With love, from

dj Brown

Written by
Joan Kerber

Illustrated by
Gloria Gedeon

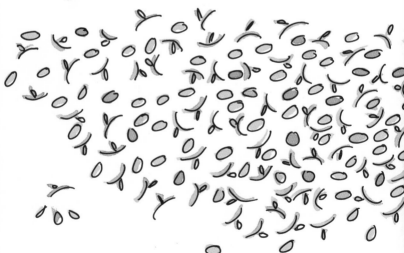

How Much Do I Love You?

THIS MUCH...

Count the
raindrops as they fall...

Count the shoppers at the mall...

Count the fishes in the sea...

Count the reruns on TV...

Count the
bears in Yellowstone...

Count the diets that are blown...

Count the words
    in windy speeches...

Count the seashells
on the beaches...

Count the paintings
at the Met...

Count the rivets on a jet...

Count the Joneses,
Smiths, and Greens...

Count the Easter jelly beans...

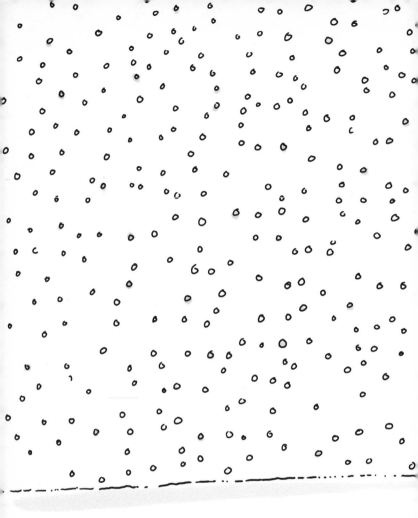

Count the snowflakes...

Count the miles
from here to Mars...

Add it up
and when you're through,
You'll know how much
I LOVE YOU!

3/5/2002

ODE to Old-debb:

You are so lovely to
                    see,...
the best part of between
        1 and 3,...

And as the distance from
        young to special grows
                wider,...

The space between us
                gets closer,...

Happy Birthday
        Grow-Old-With-Me
                Mate...

                Love, JS